Contents

Nelson's Column 2

Marble Arch 2

Buckingham Palace 4

Big Ben 6

Globe Theatre 8

Tower Bridge 10

Tower of London 12

St Paul's Cathedral 14

Covent Garden 16

Statue of Eros 18

Nelson's Column again . . .20

Glossary 24

Follow the pigeons around London. Work out which way they fly (or look at the answers, which are upside down at the bottom of the page).

The pigeons on Nelson's Column were hungry.

So they flew off to Marble Arch to look for food.

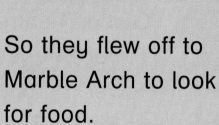

Nelson's Column

Marble Arch

Which way did they fly?

Nelson's Column is in square C3.

Marble Arch is in square C1.

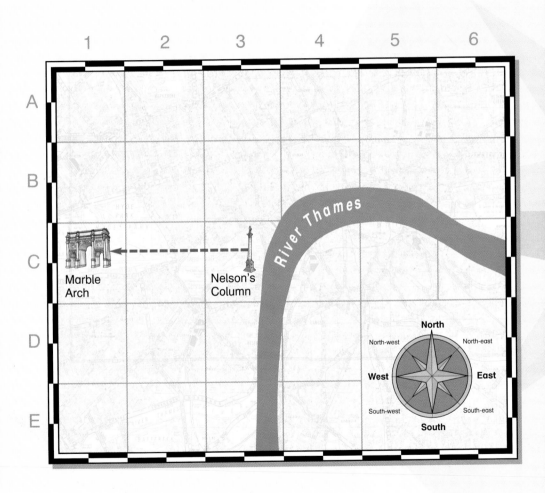

They flew West.

3

But they were scared
by the traffic.

So they flew to Buckingham Palace.

Which way did they fly?
Buckingham Palace is in square E2.

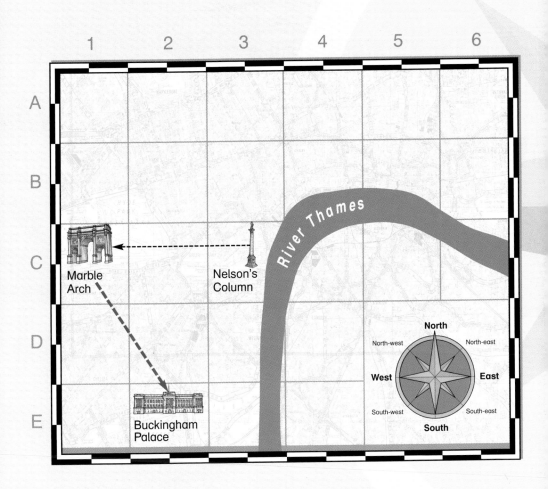

They flew South-east.

5

But they were scared
by the band.

So they flew
to Big Ben.

Which way did they fly?
Big Ben is in square E3.

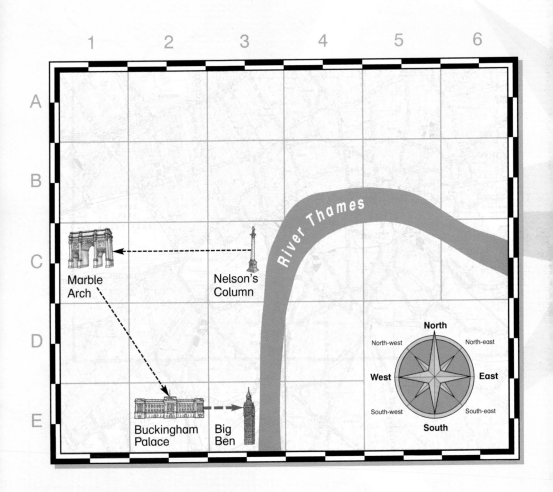

They flew East.

But they were
scared by the bell.

So they flew to
the Globe Theatre.

Which way did they fly?
The Globe Theatre is in square C5.

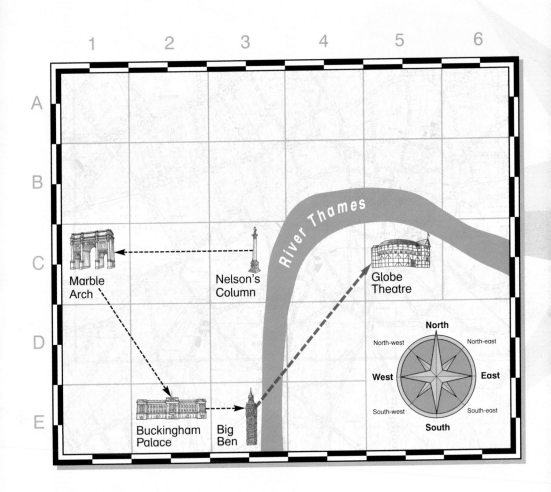

They flew North-east.

9

But they were scared
by the actors.

So they flew to
Tower Bridge.

Which way did they fly?
Tower Bridge is in square C6.

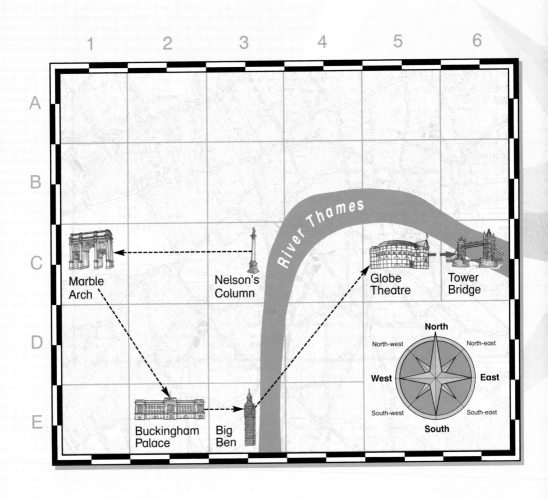

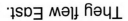
They flew East.

But they were scared
by the bridge opening.

So they flew to the
Tower of London.

Which way did they fly?
The Tower of London is in square B6.

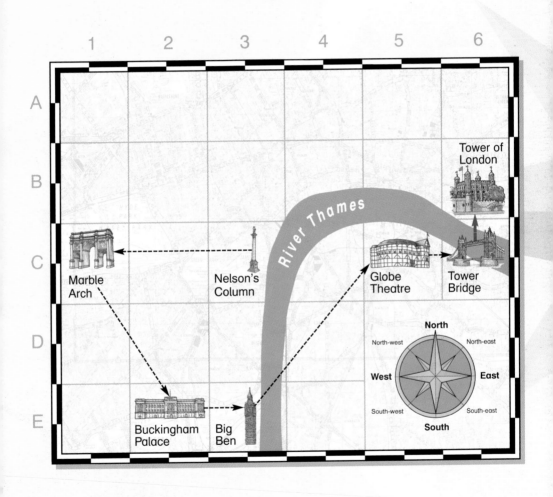

They flew North.

But they were scared by the ravens.

So they flew to St Paul's Cathedral.

Which way did they fly?
St Paul's Cathedral is in square A5.

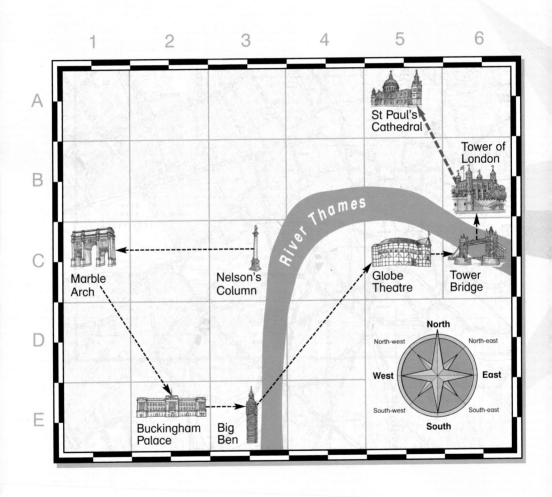

They flew North-west.

15

But they were scared
by the choirboys.

So they flew to Covent Garden.

Which way did they fly?

Covent Garden is in square A3.

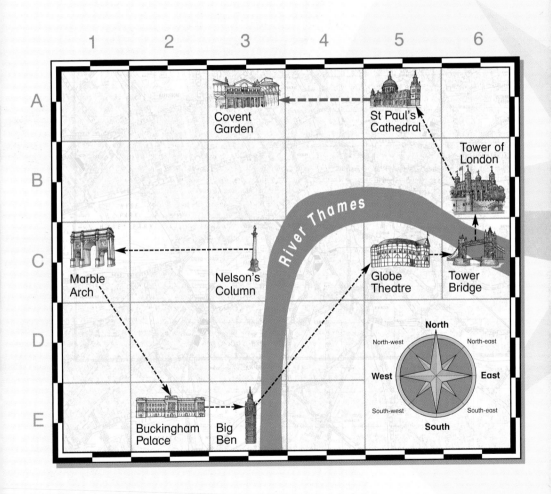

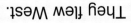

They flew West.

But they were scared
by the roadsweeper.

So they flew to the
statue of Eros.

Which way did they fly?
The statue of Eros is in square B2.

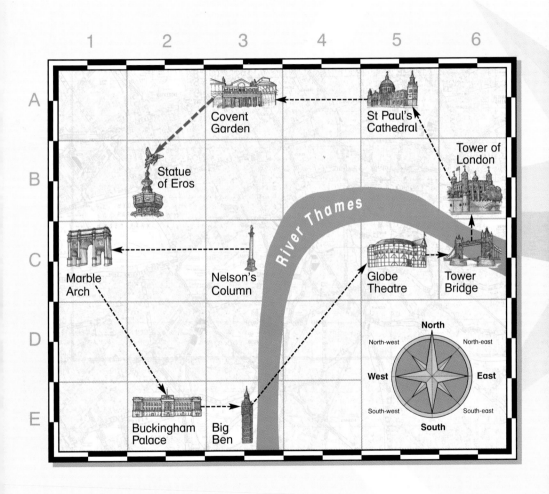

They flew South-west.

But they were scared
by the bow.

So they flew back to
Nelson's Column ...

... where the
food had arrived.

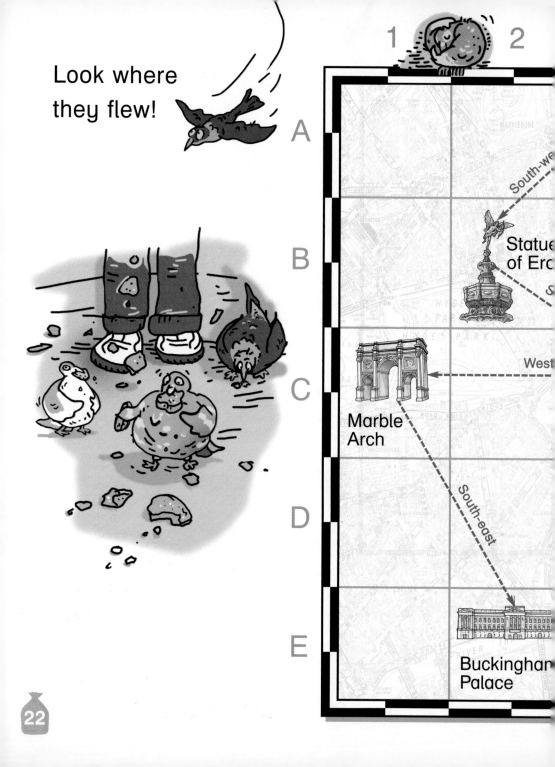

Look where they flew!

A

B Statue of Ero

C Marble Arch West

D South-east

E Buckingham Palace

1 2

South-we

22

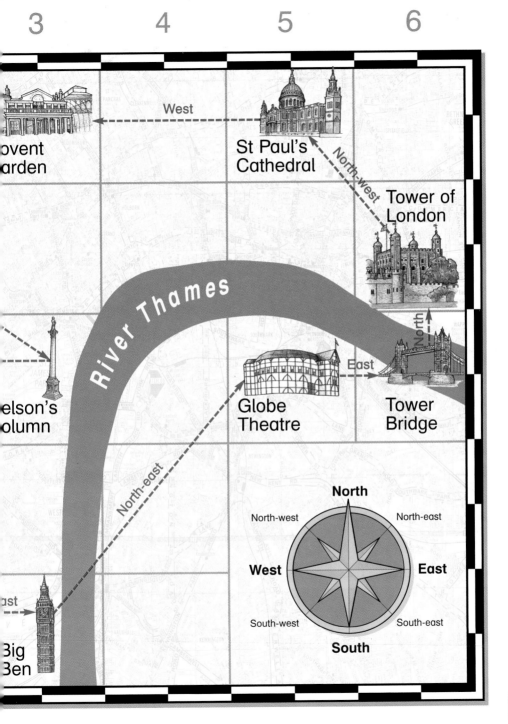

West

ovent
arden

St Paul's
Cathedral

North-west

Tower of
London

River Thames

North

elson's
olumn

Globe
Theatre

East

Tower
Bridge

North-east

ast

Big
Ben

North

North-west

North-east

West

East

South-west

South-east

South

Glossary

Big Ben

Nelson's Column

Buckingham Palace

Statue of Eros

Covent Garden

St Paul's Cathedral

Globe Theatre

Tower Bridge

Marble Arch

Tower of London